Aaron Friedrick

THE ADVENTURES OF
PETER
AND
LEISEL
A Lesson in Obedience

Book 2

Adventures of Peter and Leisel
Book 2: A Lesson in Obedience

ISBN 978-1-84625-280-8

Text and Illustrations by Aaron Friedrick
Cover illustration colorized by Michael Regina

Printed by Orchard Press Cheltenham Ltd

Dedication

To Corissa—my bride, supporter, friend, and love

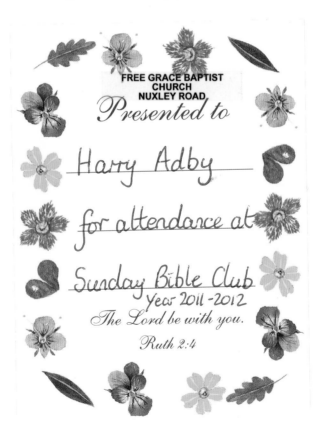

Note to the Reader

Dear Friend and Parent,

The book you are about to read was designed on two biblical assumptions. First is that God is supreme and His Word is authoritative and sufficient for all matters of life and godliness *(2 Timothy 3:16-17)*. Thus, it is the supreme duty and joy of the adult to teach children God's Word as those seeking to raise children in the training and admonition of the Lord.

The second biblical assumption is that children, unless redeemed, live with a heart in bondage to sin *(Psalm 51:5; Romans 3:23)*. Even so, there remains an innocence that permits a vivid imagination. Indeed, the imagination of a child is a wonderful thing! Because of sin, he needs God's truth to transform his heart *(Hebrews 4:12)*. This book uses the child's imagination as a portal to his heart. Through this portal, much knowledge and truth can be imparted.

You will notice that the book is divided into four chapters, each of which concludes with an application page to help the child think through the topic at hand: obedience. Additionally, throughout all the books in the series, various aspects of the gospel are addressed.

My sincere desire is that this book will serve as a tool for imparting godly wisdom to children. May you and the children you teach grow in the grace of our wonderful Lord and Savior Jesus Christ!

CHAPTER 1

Timidy was mad. His mother had just told him to not leave the back yard and he thought that this was quite unfair. He was the curious and adventurous sort. And while there was much to do in his own back yard, he imagined all the fun to be had exploring the far reaches of Pothering Woods which surrounded his home. He just simply didn't want to stay in the back yard.

As Timidy sat there pouting and feeling rather sorry for himself, he heard his friend, Badden, whistling from a distance.

Badden was the most reddish-looking little squirrel you ever saw, and he was always in trouble for some kind of mischief. He came up the path and said, "Say, Timidy, why so sad?"

With a mopey voice, Timidy told him he wasn't allowed to leave the back yard.

Badden replied, "Come on, Timidy, I'm heading to the creek. Come with me for a little bit. No one will know you were even gone."

Timidy considered the fun creek. Plus, he thought, no harm would come if he just left for a few minutes. So he hopped over the fence and scampered off with Badden.

Badden and Timidy played in the creek. A creek is a wonderful place for any young squirrel looking for adventure.

Slippery frogs to be caught;

Turtles that look like stepping stones;

Rocks to be skipped and plunked;

Fish that wiggle and jump.

Timidy was having so much fun he lost track of time... that is until he heard the faint cry of his mother calling for him in the distance.

Timidy raced home. He passed Mrs. Badger planting flowers in her front yard. He passed Mr. Mole who popped up from the ground in front of him and nearly tripped him. The voice of his mother grew louder and louder and Timidy knew that he was in trouble.

Timidy bounded over the fence of his back yard only to see his mother looking sternly at him. She scolded him for not obeying and said, "Timidy, if you don't listen and obey, some day you are going to get hurt."

STOP AND THINK!

Timidy thought that it wasn't a big deal to disobey his mother by leaving the back yard.
What does God think of disobedience?

What God says in the Bible:

"The LORD detests the way of the wicked, but he loves those who pursue godliness."
Proverbs 15:9 (NLT)

Disobedience is sin. Sin is always a big deal. To disobey your parents or God's commands is to disobey God Himself. The wicked are those who sin against God and don't care that they are sinning. God hates sin, but He deeply loves those who obey Him.

CHAPTER 2

The next day, Timidy sat once again confined to his
back yard. Timidy thought about the creek and all of
the new places in the woods he had not yet explored.
He knew he should obey his mother, but the more he
thought about it, the more he wanted to go to the creek.

Soon he wanted to leave the back yard so badly, he
could hardly stand it. Timidy looked around. No one was
watching. Then, in a split second, he jumped over the
fence and scurried off to the creek.

When Timidy arrived at the creek, he felt very alone and quite bad for disobeying his mother. The frogs and rocks that were so much fun before weren't quite as exciting now.

Timidy was about to go home when something caught his eye. Just past the creek he saw a faint glow disappear into the woods. What was it? Curious, Timidy followed it deeper into the forest. Suddenly he found himself surrounded by a swarm of fireflies which looked like a cloud of twinkling stars.

The fireflies soon disappeared. Timidy looked around and realized that he was lost (which is not a very fun feeling to have). He tried to turn toward home, but no matter which way he turned, he couldn't figure out which way to go. Timidy panicked! But then he heard voices in the distance.

Timidy followed the voices until he arrived at a clearing in the forest. He cautiously peered out from the trees, and to his surprise he saw two children playing behind their house. Could it be? Why yes, it was Peter and Leisel!

Timidy sat there watching Peter and Leisel. The animals of Pothering Woods had wondered what had happened to Peter after he had gone to the Dragon's Lair looking for Leisel. Since Peter had never returned, they thought that the Dragon had probably gotten him and, of course, they were so scared of the Dragon that they did not dare go and look for him.

But here were Peter and Leisel. Timidy looked around and didn't see any sign of the Dragon. He was very happy that Peter was able to rescue Leisel from the Dragon. He was about to go to them when he heard a deep, low growl behind him.

STOP AND THINK!

Timidy was tempted to leave the back yard.
**What are some things you have been tempted to do
that are wrong?**

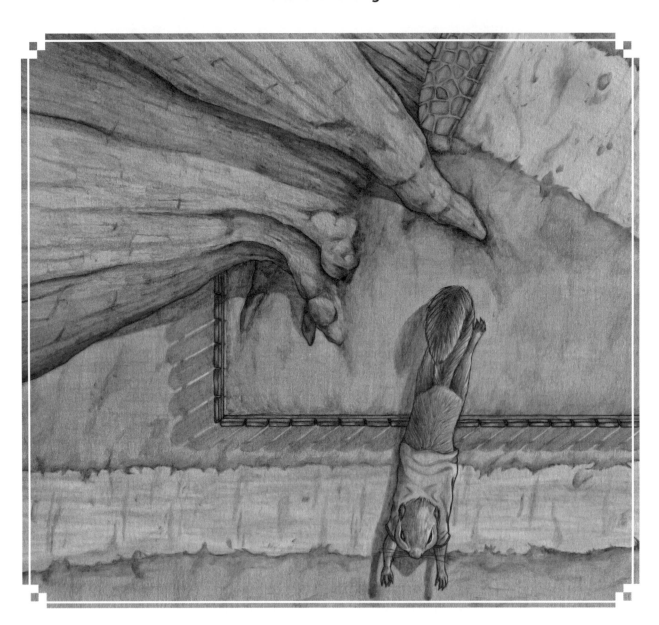

What God says in the Bible:

"The temptations in your life are no different from what others experience. And God is faithful. He will not allow the temptation to be more than you can stand. When you are tempted, he will show you a way out so that you can endure."
I Corinthians 10:13 (NLT)

Everyone deals with temptation. When you are tempted, you want to do the things that are wrong. God promises that there is no temptation which you won't be able to handle. God always provides a way to escape the temptation for those who love and obey Him.

CHAPTER 3

Timidy turned toward the growl. He couldn't see anything. His heart began to pound wildly. He heard the growl again, this time closer. He froze with fright. Every hair on his body stood up. Still, he couldn't see anything.

Then out of the corner of his eye, he spotted a little movement. Slowly, he turned toward it and looked into the shadows. Nothing. Wait! There it was! To his horror, Timidy saw in the distance the shadow of a dark wolf.

The wolf didn't move. It was just staring at him. Or was it? Timidy couldn't tell if it was looking at him or at something else. He was, after all, pretty small and the wolf was still far away. But then it began to inch toward him staying very low to the ground. Timidy could now see its angry yellow eyes and how huge it was.

Timidy had never been so scared in his life. His mind told him to run but his legs wouldn't move. The wolf kept getting closer...and closer...and closer.

Timidy finally bolted and began running as fast as he could.

The wolf let out a hideous shriek. It sounded something like a growl, a bark, and a howl all mixed together. Timidy dashed through the forest. He heard the wolf behind him getting closer. It was much faster.

Timidy made his little legs go as fast as they could. He dodged a stump, sprang over a log, and tumbled through a bush. The wolf crashed through the same bush right behind him and snarled a hideous snarl.

Faster Timidy! Go faster!

Timidy raced forward, dashing to the left and to the right. With every move he made, the wolf gained on him. A wide stream was ahead. Timidy didn't know if he could jump over it. He raced to the edge of the stream, leapt with all his might, and sailed over it to the other side. Splash! The wolf plunged through the stream and pounced on Timidy. He felt the wolf's teeth grab his tail. Timidy pulled with all his might, wiggled free, and shot off running again. The wolf howled and sprang after him. The trees! Fleeing for his life, Timidy had not thought about the trees. He turned toward the nearest tree and scurried into its branches. Safe! At least for now.

STOP AND THINK!

Timidy was in danger because he disobeyed his mother.
What are some of the bad things that can happen when you disobey your parents?

What God says in the Bible:

"For the wages of sin is death, but the free gift of God is eternal life through Christ Jesus our Lord."
Romans 6:23 (NLT)

All men, women, and children sin—they disobey God. Sin is rebellion against God and bad things always happen when you sin. God is holy (without any sin) and must punish sin. This is the worst consequence of sin. But God is very loving and has provided heaven and the forgiveness of sins through His Son, Jesus.

CHAPTER 4

Timidy peered down at the wolf as it circled the tree, snarling. He thought that he might be able to escape by jumping from tree to tree. But as he looked around, he saw that the closest tree was too far away. He was safe from the wolf, but he was quite stuck.

As he was trying to figure out what to do next, he heard the cry of an eagle. Appearing from nowhere, a large eagle swooped in and landed next to him.

Timidy didn't move a muscle. Timidy was scared, but the Eagle seemed familiar. Timidy thought that he might be the Eagle of the Great Pine, but he wasn't sure. He felt fearful and safe all at the same time.

"Do you know why you're here, Timidy?" asked the Eagle.

Timidy was surprised that the Eagle knew his name. But then he thought about how he had disobeyed his mother and now he wished that he was safe in his back yard.

The Eagle then said, "Climb into my claw and I will take you to safety."

Timidy wasn't so sure about this offer.

Timidy asked, "How do I know that you are a good eagle?"

"I am," said the Eagle.

Timidy looked down at the wolf. "How do I know you won't eat me?" he asked the Eagle.

"Because if I was going to eat you, I would have done it by now," said the Eagle.

"How can I trust you?" Timidy finally asked.

The Eagle seemed to smile as he said, "Because I am giving you trust."

Timidy couldn't explain it, but he knew he could trust the Eagle. He cautiously climbed into the Eagle's claw with razor sharp talons. The Eagle glanced at the scowling wolf, gently closed his talons around Timidy, and launched into the sky with his great wings.

The Eagle quickly rose high into the sky. Timidy was amazed that he could see all of Pothering Woods. He could even see his home in the distance.

The Eagle soon landed near Timidy's home. Timidy happily thanked the Eagle and ran home as fast as he could.

He arrived home and found all the animals of Pothering Woods gathered together. Timidy had been gone for quite some time and they were forming a search party to look for him. Everyone was very glad to see him, especially his mother.

Timidy told them everything that had happened. Then he went up to his mother and asked for forgiveness for his disobedience. His mother forgave him and gave him a great big hug.

STOP AND THINK!

Timidy almost lost his life because of his disobedience.
What do you think he learned in this story?

What God says in the Bible:

**"Praise the LORD! How joyful are those who fear the
LORD and delight in obeying his commands."**
Psalm 112:1 (NLT)

When you disobey God and the people who care
for you, you are putting yourself in danger. When you
are disobedient, you will always be very unhappy. But
when you are obedient to God, you will be most happy
and safe.

BIBLICAL STORY

Consequences of Disobedience

Numbers 21:4-9

The Israelites often disobeyed God. Once, while they were wandering in the wilderness, they complained greatly against God. They complained that God rescued them out of Egypt. They accused God of bringing them into the wilderness to die. They whined about the food and grumbled about the water. By complaining, they disobeyed the command to honor and respect God.

To punish the Israelites for their disobedient complaining, God sent poisonous snakes into their camp.

The whole camp became filled with snakes. The snakes bit the people and many of them died or got very sick. So the people came to Moses and cried out, "We have sinned, because we have spoken against the LORD."

God heard their cry. To save the people, God told Moses to make a bronze snake and set it on a pole. When the Israelites looked up at it in faith, they were healed of their snake bites.

God punishes sin, but He also provides a way to escape His punishment through Jesus. Just like the bronze snake which was raised on a pole, Jesus was raised on a cross and crucified. Jesus didn't deserve to die because He always obeyed God—He never sinned. But we disobey God and deserve to die and be punished forever. Jesus is the only one who can save us from such a bad end.

Note to reader: Please see Books 3 and 4 (forthcoming) for more on the gospel.